SWR explained

A Radio Amateurs' Guide to Electromagnetic Waves,
Transmission Lines and VSWR

By

R T Irish, G4LUF

Radio Society of Great Britain

Published by the Radio Society of Great Britain, 3 Abbey Court, Fraser Road, Priory Business Park, Bedford MK44 3WH. Tel 01234 832700 Web www.rsgb.org

First published 2014

Reprinted 2015 & 2017

Editing and Layout: Mike Browne, G3DIH

Cover Design: Kevin Williams, M6CYB

Production: Mark Allgar, M1MPA

Printed in Great Britain by Hobbs the Printers Ltd of Totton, Hampshire

ISBN: 9781 9050 8699 3

Contents

Acknowledgements

It is a pleasure to acknowledge the continuous support and encouragement given by my wife, Clare, during the preparation of this material, the much-appreciated efforts of my son, George, who has sorted out my many computer problems and my daughter, Polly, who has shown great patience over recent weeks. All are gratefully acknowledged. *Sine qui nihil.*

The subject of waves and transmission lines can quickly develop into quite a complex subject but the author has tried, as far as possible, to minimise any necessary mathematics and to present the material in an attractively descriptive manner. Almost inevitably, some of this mathematics has crept in towards the end and it is hoped that will be acceptable to most readers.

The supporting mathematics for the material within this book has not been abandoned and appears in the appendices for those readers who are already familiar with the solution of electrical network problems.

Reg Irish, G4LUF
2014

Introduction

Whilst studying the properties of electromagnetic waves and transmission lines in my youth, I was very challenged by the conventional approach to the topic, which involved extremely heavy mathematics.

Since then there has been little change in this approach which does tend to leave those who are interested, but not well versed in the mathematics, rather at a loss. It has always been felt that a largely descriptive, alternative approach would be most useful and provide a worthwhile initial insight into the topic.

We are all familiar with the general idea of what a wave is - often from experiences with waves on the sea. However, as with many apparently obvious things in life, detailed study of the topic can be surprisingly complicated.

It is hoped that this book will provide a useful, initial introduction both for the radio amateur and others starting out on the topic, to get a practical "feel" for the subject.

The bulk of the material has therefore been made descriptive in nature with most of the occasionally-necessary mathematical material appearing in the appendices for those already familiar with the solution of electrical network problems.

Reg Irish, G4LUF
2014

1

A General Introduction to Waves

It is hoped that this publication will introduce some of the more important properties of waves in general, and also some of the aspects which are particularly relevant to understanding the main properties of electromagnetic waves.

As a child at the seaside, most of us watched the waves on the surface of the sea, noticing the way in which they travel in a specific direction. A little later in life, perhaps as a rod and line angler, we might have noticed that a float on the water's surface does not travel with the wave, but rises and falls (almost) vertically as the wave travels past - Fig. 1.1 below:

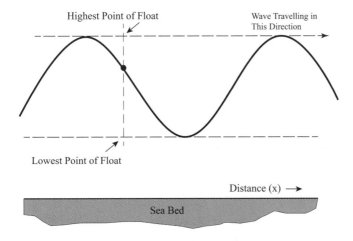

Fig. 1.1 A Simple Water Wave

Continuing our observations of the float, we may deduce that any particle of water within the wave will also move up and down in a similar manner, as suggested in Fig. 1.1 above. This particle will, in general therefore, have some energy due to its velocity (kinetic energy). At the instant when the particle is at the peak of the wave it is momentarily stationary, with no energy due to its velocity - but it will have some energy due to its position (potential energy). As the wave sweeps past, both of these quantities vary in a direction which is **perpendicular** to the direction in which the wave is moving. This type of wave is therefore known as a **transverse** wave and is typical of most types of electromagnetic waves which we will be considering in later chapters.

Returning to Fig. 1.1 again, it will be realised that there are three very significant factors about the wave:

1. They travel across the surface in one specific direction. In the case of water waves the speed at which they travel is determined by the water depth - waves in the deep ocean are large and widely spread, whilst those in shallow water are much closer together. In the case of electromagnetic waves, their speed depends upon the electrical characteristics of the medium through which they travel (principally the relative permittivity of this medium). As expected, the symbol for velocity is "v".

The velocity of radio waves is 300,000,000m/s (3.10^8m/s) - a figure it is useful to be able to recall for future use.

2. If a photograph is taken of the sea's surface, we see a regular, gently-undulating surface, varying with distance (x), in the direction of travel of the waves. The distance between adjacent wave peaks is known as the **wavelength** (symbol λ , normally expressed in metres) of the waves. This is obviously the same as the distance between successive troughs - or, indeed, between any corresponding points between two waves - see Fig. 1.2

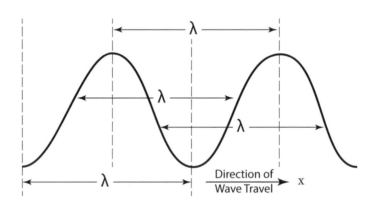

Fig. 1.2 The Wavelength (λ) of a Wave

3. If one stands in the sea, the waves will sweep past, moving regularly up and down one's legs as they do so. The number of waves passing in one second is known as the **frequency** of the waves (symbol f). This is measured in Hertz (Hz is the abbreviation), although c/s - cycles per second may be encountered in earlier texts on waves.

Amateur radio commonly uses waves whose frequency is many thousands, millions or even thousands of millions of Hz and it is usual to express these as multiples of ten by using prefixes, as below:

Prefix	Abbreviation	Multiplier	Example
Kilo	k	$1,000 = 10^3$	2kHz = 2,000Hz
Mega	M	$1,000,000 = 10^6$	14MHz = 14,000,000Hz
Giga	G	$1,000,000,000 = 10^9$	2.1Ghz = 2,100,000,000Hz

Other multiple prefixes do exist, but are not usually of interest as they are outside the amateur's range of interest. In summary, waves of a frequency f Hz, travel in a specific direction with a velocity (v), in a regular wave pattern, described by the wavelength (λ).

There is an important relationship between these three quantities, v, f and λ. Fig 1.3. shows a transmitter emitting waves. As has already been discussed, the distance between similar parts of successive waves is the wavelength (λ)

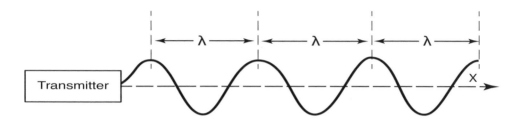

Fig, 1.3 Snapshot of a One Second Transmission

As shown in this diagram, the transmitter is emitting waves whose wavelength is λ m.

In one second there are f cycles passing an observer. The distance travelled by the leading part of the first wave (at X in Fig. 1.3) in one second is therefore f.λ m. This is the wave's velocity, v (distance travelled per second). Therefore

$$v = f.\lambda$$

The usefulness of this simple equation is illustrated by the frequent necessity of finding either f or λ when the other is known. For example, to find the wavelength of a 14.1 MHz transmission (knowing that $v = 3.10^8$m/s).

Therefore $\lambda = v /f = 3.10^8 / (14.1.10^6) = 21.3$m (the 20m band).

This is important information as the size of the antenna is normally related to the wavelength.

The reader may care to consider an associated calculation - to find the frequency of a radio wave whose wavelength is 3cm (0.03m).   (Answer: 10GHz).

2

Electromagnetic Waves in Free Space

Electromagnetic waves: An electromagnetic wave is an example of a transverse wave - as discussed in Chapter 1. There are two quantities, linked to each other, associated with this wave:

1. An electric field (E) Fig. 2.1, shows two parallel, flat plates separated by a distance d and connected to a voltage source V (Volts). Between these plates the air will be subjected to an electric field of V/d Volts/m. If this field strength is very large (ie. if V is very large or if d is very small) the air between the plates may break down, with arcing taking place between them. The air between them is simply stressed by the electric field. The symbol for electric field is E and this has units of Volts per metre (V/m.). Hence E = V/d. The transmission of a radio wave is associated with such electric fields and, as may be expected, if this field has too high a value, the air may break down. This may be a problem where high power energy is concerned (for example in radar systems) and the whole guiding system is often filled with pressurised air to increase the sustainable electric field before breakdown occurs.

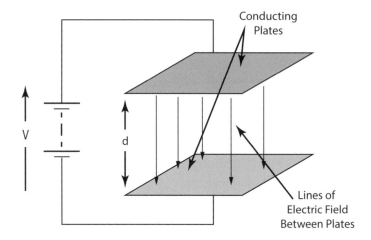

Fig. 2.1 An Electric Field

2. A magnetic field (symbol H). Magnetic fields are normally generated by a current-carrying conductor. The diagram (Fig. 2.2) shows the magnetic field associated with such a conductor - it is suspected that amateurs will already be familiar with this effect and probably will have encountered the concept when considering the working principles of the electric motor.

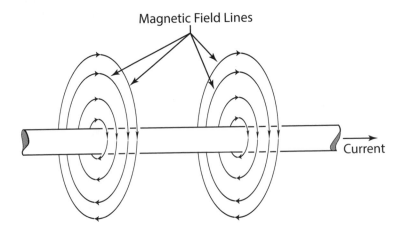

Magnetic Field Lines

Current

Fig. 2.2 Magnetic Field Lines Surrounding a Current-Carrying Conductor

The units of magnetic field are Ampères per metre (A/m). In radio practice, such magnetic fields are principally of interest far away from their originating conductors, where the field lines are effectively straight. An electromagnetic wave in free space consists of two component parts, an electric field (E) and a magnetic field (H). Both quantities rise and fall together (as do the water waves discussed in Chapter 1), but they are at right angles to each other and to the direction of the wave's propagation - as shown in Fig. 2.3 below.

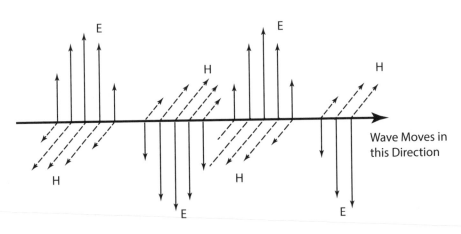

Wave Moves in this Direction

Fig. 2.3 The Electromagnetic Wave in Free Space

By considering this simple diagram, we may readily appreciate that an antenna designed to interact with the electric field (eg. a dipole) will not pick up any signal if it is aligned with the H-field. Similarly, if a receiving loop, which principally interacts with the magnetic field, is aligned to interact with the electric field of the wave, it will receive nothing.

For a transmission over the earth, the direction of the electric field is called the **polarisation** of the wave. Thus, a vertically-polarised wave will have its electric field perpendicular to the earth's surface (eg. 2m repeater transmissions) as in Fig. 2.3 Similarly, a horizontally-polarised wave will have the E-field along the earth's surface and the magnetic field will then lie perpendicular to the earth's surface, (eg. fm radio broadcast transmissions). It is interesting to note that the two fields, E and H are linked by the simple equation:

$$E/H = Z_0$$

where Z_0 is known as the characteristic impedance of free space and has a value of 377 Ohms (120π). Also notice from Fig. 2.3 that the direction of propagation of the wave is given by the direction in which a corkscrew would travel when turning from the direction of E to the direction of H (try it for yourself using Fig. 2.3)

One important factor, when considering electromagnetic waves is their "strength". Is the wave too weak to be detected by a distant receiver? At any distance r from a transmitter, the wave power flowing through one square metre is known as the intensity, I, of the wave, measured in Watts/square metre (W/m^2). Fig. 2.4 below shows a transmitter, radiating a power P_T Watts and initially assumed to transmit equally in all directions, with a receiver at a range r metres.

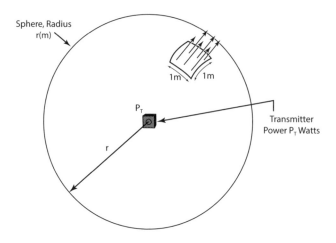

Fig. 2.4 The Inverse Square Law

The surface area of a sphere, radius r, surrounding the transmitter is $4\pi r^2$ and the power flowing through one square metre of this area is therefore $P_T/4\pi r^2$ Watts per square metre. This is the intensity (I) of the wave at this distance from the transmitter.

Thus:

$$I = \frac{P_T}{4\pi r^2}$$

To illustrate the importance of this simple formula, consider a transmitter, power P_T, a receiver initially at range r and receiving a signal intensity I_1. If the receiver is now moved to twice the original range, ie. to 2r and also the transmitter power remains the same, the new intensity, I_2 will be given by

$$I_2 = P_T/4\pi(2r)^2 = I_1/4$$

ie. the intensity at this new range is reduced to one quarter of the original intensity. Similarly, if the range of the receiver is trebled, the signal intensity will be reduced to one ninth of the original intensity ($1/3^2$). Increasing the range by five times will reduce the intensity by twenty five times..etc. Going the other way, reducing the range to one half of the original will increase the intensity by four times. An associated problem frequently arises in which it is required to know the increase in transmitter power necessary to increase the maximum receiving range of a received signal by a known amount. In this case the intensities of the signal are the same, both are receiving a just-detectable signal intensity. As an example, let us find the increase in transmitter power necessary to double the maximum receiver range. Initially,

$I_1 = P_{T1}/4\pi r_1^2$ and at the increased range $I_2 = P_{T2}/4\pi r_2^2$, where P_{T1} and P_{T2} are the transmitted powers at ranges r_1 and r_2 respectively. However, these intensities are both the same (a just detectable signal) and $r_2 = 2r_1$. From the second of these equations it is obviously necessary to make $P_{T2} = 4P_{T1}$ to get back to the original intensity, the "4s" cancelling out.

Although these fairly straightforward calculations are certainly good for working out the range, transmitter power and intensity of a signal, in practice the results often vary significantly due to other effects - such as reflections from the ionosphere, intervening terrain, ground effects and notably at VHF and above, the detailed weather conditions.

3

Guided Electromagnetic Waves

There is often a requirement to transport electromagnetic wave energy from one location to another with the minimum possible energy loss - eg. from a transmitter to its antenna. This energy may be guided using a wide variety of systems, the most common of which are the coaxial line and the open twin feeder. These and some of the many other wave guiding arrangements which may be encountered in practice are outlined in Appendix A.

Waves in both coaxial lines and in open twin feeder are essentially transverse electromagnetic waves, ie. their electric and magnetic fields are both perpendicular to their direction of propagation and also to each other - as are such waves in free space (see Chapter 2). However, they are confined by a metallic conductor arrangement which ensures that they are not subject to the spreading effects $(1/r^2)$ of such waves in free space. There are two important points to appreciate here:

1. The velocity of the waves will be, generally, less than it would be in a vacuum (or in air). This is largely attributable to the dielectric constant (relative permittivity) of the material through which the waves travel. In general, the velocity (v) is given by:

$$v = c/\sqrt{\varepsilon_r}$$

where c is the waves' velocity in a vacuum (3.10^8 m/s) and ε_r is the relative permittivity of the insulating material. Tables of the values of this relative dielectric constant for a range of materials are readily available in many textbooks and on the internet - a few of the more common ones are shown in Table 3.1 below:

Material	Relative Permittivity
Dry air	1.0006
Glass	approx. 5.0
P.T.F.E.	2.0
Polythene	2.3

Table 3.1 Some Common Materials and Their Relative Permittivity

2. In a guided wave system, the electrostatic and magnetic fields are, respectively, directly associated with the voltage between the conductors and the currents in them. In the same way as the ratio E/H is fixed for waves in free space (Chapter 2) as Z_0, the characteristic impedance of free space, so in the case of guided systems, the ratio of the voltage across

the conductors to the current in the conductors is fixed. This is called the characteristic impedance of the system (symbol Z_0),

$$\text{ie } V/I = Z_0$$

everywhere on the line. This is entirely governed by the geometry of the system.

Some standard results for common lines are shown in Appendix B. In the cases of the commonly used coaxial line and the open twin line, these characteristic impedances are usually in the order of 30 to 200 Ohms and 150 to 600 Ohms respectively. Since these two types of transmission line are the most commonly used, a short consideration of their characteristics is appropriate here:

1. The Coaxial Line

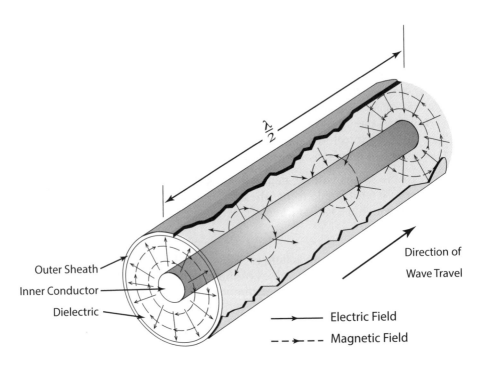

Fig.3.1 Electromagnetic Waves in a Coaxial Cable

This form of wave guiding system consists of a central conductor, surrounded by a cylindrical conducting sheath - as indicated in Fig.3.1 above. The outer conductor is normally a closely-woven copper wire sheath, making the arrangement quite flexible. For extremely high powers, solid inner conductors and outer sheaths may be used but, as may be expected, there is little or no mechanical flexibility with such systems. The presence of the outer sheath ensures that both the electric and magnetic fields are confined within the cable and this cable may therefore be used in the proximity of metallic objects - guttering, metal window frames etc. without affecting its operation. (This contrasts with the open twin feeder, to be described later in this chapter.) As has been outlined, the ratio between the voltage, between the conductors and the current in them, is called the characteristic impedance (symbol Z_0) and depends solely upon the ratio of the radius of the inner conductor to the radius of the outer conductor (sheath). The formula for this is

$$Z_0 = 138 \log_{10}(R/r) \text{ Ohms}$$

where R is the inner radius of the sheath and r is the radius of the inner conductor. Often the space between these conductors is filled with a plastic supporting material, frequently a foam, and the characteristic impedance given by the above should then be divided by the square root of the relative permittivity of the filling.

2. The Open Twin Line

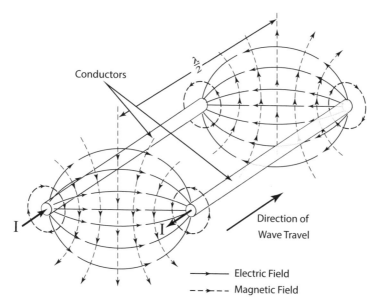

Fig. 3.2 Electromagnetic Waves on Open Twin Feeder

This is the simplest type of transmission line, consisting simply of two parallel conductors, maintained at a constant spacing along their length (Fig. 3.2 above). This spacing is usually achieved by the use of individual "spreaders", set regularly along the length of the line or by a narrow plastic web arrangement. It is worth noting that this spacing between the conductors should be kept to a value which is less than about 1/16th to 1/20th of a wavelength. Wider spacing than this results in a significant amount of energy radiation from these feeders. The wave is propagated as a simple transverse electromagnetic wave - as has already been discussed. However, it is obvious from Fig. 3.2 that the electric and magnetic fields are not closely confined to the conductors, but extend some distance around them. This implies that care should be taken not to interfere with these fields by running the line near or over metallic objects - such as metallic guttering or wiring systems. The characteristic impedance (Z_0) of this line is given by

$$Z_0 = 276 \log_{10}(2D/d)$$

where D is the spacing between the centres of the two conductors and d is the diameter of the conductors themselves.

Losses in Wave Guiding Systems

In practice, there are three principal sources of energy loss in these systems:

1. Resistive losses (I^2R) in the conductors. Although the metal concerned is usually copper - a good conductor - it does have some resistance which absorbs some of the power passing through. The effective resistance does vary with frequency and it is worth noting that this may be significantly higher than the resistance at dc. This is due to the tendency of high frequency currents to flow on the outside "skin" of the conductor, rather than uniformly throughout its cross-sectional area.

2. Losses in the dielectric material supporting the conductors. These may be minimised by the careful choice of the type of cable but, again, these will not be the same for all frequencies.

3. Radiation losses from coaxial cable are likely to be very small, but it should be appreciated that some leakage, even through the closely-woven sheath, does occur. In the case of the open twin line, some small amount of direct radiation does occur but this may be minimised by keeping the conductor spacing small compared to the wavelength of the propagating energy.

4

Standing Waves on Transmission Line Systems

In chapters 1 and 2, we have seen that a travelling electromagnetic wave in a guided system consists of both a voltage wave and an associated current wave. The relationship between this voltage and current is everywhere given by

$$V/I = Z_o$$

where Z_o is called the characteristic impedance of the line (this is effectively resistive for high frequency lines where the losses may normally be neglected). This is shown in Fig. 4.1:

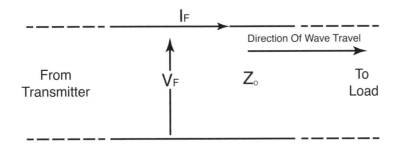

Fig. 4.1 Direction of Wave Energy Flow

In Fig. 4.1, consideration of the direction of the wave energy flow is indicated by the direction of I_F with respect to the head of the arrow representing V_F - in this diagram the wave is therefore travelling to the right. Also notice that in the absence of any other effects the measured voltage and current due to this wave on the line is **everywhere** the same, namely V_F and I_F. It is also important to note that, contrary to popular belief, the nature of the load at the end of the line does not affect these conditions.

The forward wave (V_F and I_F) now travels down towards the load. It is not an intelligent wave (!) and therefore does not know what might befall it once it arrives at the load. However, once it actually arrives at the load, the energy in the wave will split into two parts:

1. Part may be absorbed by the load itself - usually the antenna, to which we want to send the maximum possible power

2. Some fraction of the power in the forward wave may be **reflected** back up the line, towards the transmitter. This situation is shown in Fig. 4.2, where V_F and I_F are associated with the forward wave and V_R and I_R are associated with the reflected wave.

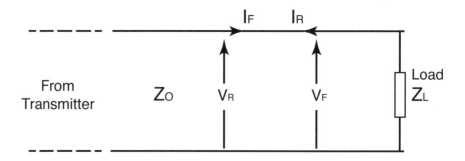

Fig. 4.2 Forward and Reverse Waves on a Transmission Line

In general therefore, there are **two** travelling waves on the line, one travelling forward towards the load, and one travelling back towards the generator (transmitter) - as in Fig. 4.2. Notice that the reflected current is in the opposite direction to the forward current because the reflected wave is travelling to the left.

Before looking at the effects of having two waves on the line, we may first investigate the factors which determine the size of the reflected wave by considering conditions at the load, Z_L.

At the load itself, the voltages V_F and V_R will simply add but the currents will **subtract** since they are going in opposite directions. Hence the voltage across the load is $V_F + V_R$ and the current is $I_F - I_R$ as shown in Fig. 4.3.

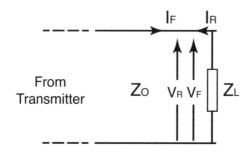

Fig. 4.3 Conditions at the Load

But the load obeys Ohm's Law so that:

$$Z_L = \frac{\text{Voltage across } Z_L}{\text{Current through } Z_L} = \frac{V_F + V_R}{I_F - I_R}$$

But each of the currents, I_F and I_R is determined by:

$$I_F = V_F/Z_o \quad \text{and} \quad I_R = V_R/Z_o$$

Substituting these expressions into the above equation for Z_L gives

$$Z_L = \frac{V_F + V_R}{\dfrac{V_F}{Z_0} - \dfrac{V_R}{Z_0}} = \frac{Z_0(V_F + V_R)}{V_F - V_R}$$

To find V_R from this, cross multiply the above to give

$$V_F Z_L - V_R Z_L = Z_o V_F + Z_o V_R$$

and re-arranging:

$$V_R (Z_L + Z_o) = V_F (Z_L - Z_o)$$

or

$$V_R = V_F \frac{Z_L - Z_o}{Z_L + Z_o}$$

The fraction in this expression is known as the voltage reflection coefficient (often simply abbreviated to "reflection coefficient"), symbol ρ - the Greek letter "r". Notice that when $Z_L = Z_o$, $\rho = 0$ all of the forward power is absorbed by the load and none is reflected back up the line - the desirable situation!

Also as we have seen, from this, if $Z_L = 0$, a short circuit, then $V_R = -V_F$ and all of the forward power is reflected back, $\rho = -1$. The negative sign simply means that the reflected wave at the load starts moving back towards the transmitter "upside down" with respect to the forward wave (see later). This ties in with the necessity for the voltage at the load to be zero (a short - circuit) and this is shown diagrammatically in (Fig. 4.4).

Similarly, with an open - circuit load, when $Z_L = \infty$, $V_R = V_F$ ($\rho = 1$) when the voltage will be twice V_F.

The other possibility for Z_L is that it is a complex impedance (ie. it consists of both resistive and reactive components), but the same principles also apply. To keep this presentation at a reasonable level, only resistive loads are considered here but complex values of ρ are easily dealt with should it be necessary.

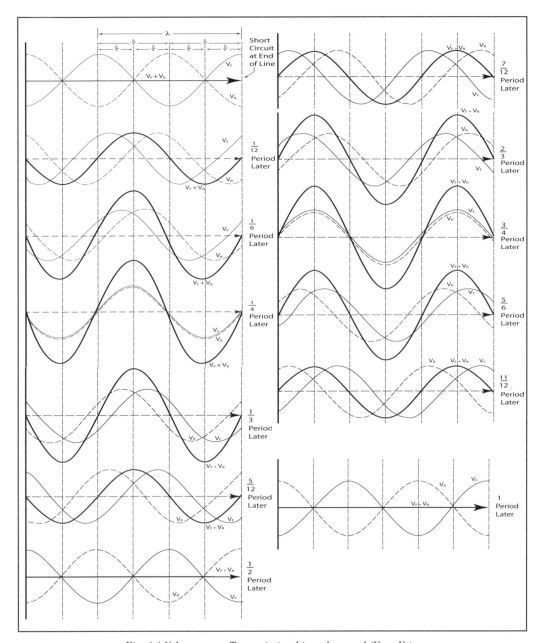

Fig. 4.4 Voltages on a Transmission Line where p=1 (V_R = V_F)

Let us now look at the effects of the waves, reflected back from the load, on the rest of the line. The topmost diagram in Fig. 4.4 shows a wave on a transmission line system which has been short - circuited at its end, ie. $Z_L = 0$. As has already been seen, the reflection coefficient (ρ) is then -1, meaning that the whole wave starts returning to the transmitter in such a way that the **total** voltage at the load is zero (consistent with a short-circuit). Examination of the right hand side of this figure illustrates this condition.

Looking back along the line also shows there to be zero total voltages at this instant. Subsequent diagrams illustrate what is happening at later times. In the second diagram, 1/12th of a cycle later (30°) the forward wave has advanced slightly towards the load and the reflected wave has moved the same distance from the load. The total voltage $(V_F + V_R)$ is not now zero, as it was in the first diagram.

The next diagram, 1/6th cycle later (60°), shows both waves to have moved even further and the total wave to be greater even than the incident wave.

In the fourth diagram the total voltage on the line $(V_F + V_R)$ can be seen to have risen to peaks which are twice the value of the forward wave. Further diagrams show what happens for the rest of the cycle - in particular notice that this total voltage wave again rises to twice that of the forward wave, but in the reverse direction. However, looking carefully at the whole set of diagrams, we can locate positions on the line where the voltages V_F and V_R are always equal and opposite and therefore cancel. These occur at the load itself, half a wavelength ($\lambda/2$) back from the load, one wavelength (λ) from the load …. ie. every half wavelength from the load.

The author was born at the seaside, and I am reminded that when we had a severe storm, very high sea waves occurred, extremely dangerous volumes of water moved up and down at the vertical edge of the promenade.

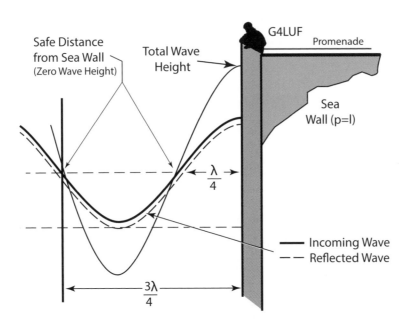

Fig. 4.5 The Author on the Promenade on a Stormy Day

It was too easy to be swept away into the sea with disastrous consequences. The edge of the sea corresponds to a point in Fig. 4.4, where the waves rise to twice the height of the forward wave alone ($\lambda/4$ back from the short-circuit load position in the first diagram). However, at a distance $\lambda/4$ out to sea, the incident and reflected water waves cancel and relatively calm water will occur. The common local advice if you are unfortunate enough to be swept away by an unusually large wave, is therefore **not** to try to struggle back to

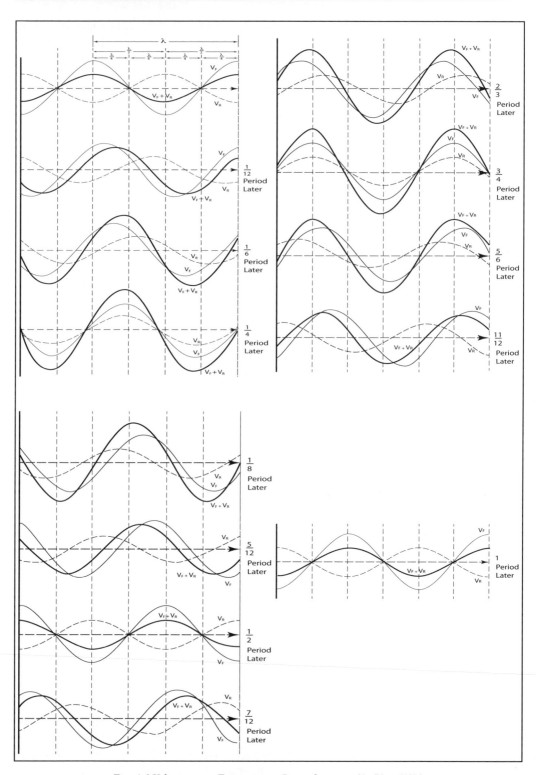

Fig. 4.6 Voltages on a Transmission Line where p = ½ (V_R = ½V_F)

the sea wall, but to strike out seawards until an area of calm water is encountered, (where the forward and reflected waves cancel) and to there await rescue!

Figure 4.6 shows the same situation, as before in Fig. 4.4, but with a reflection coefficient of -½. In a similar manner to Fig. 4.4, the reflected wave, together with the forward wave causes the total voltage to vary with distance. However, when the positive or negative peaks of the waves coincide the total voltage now rises to 1½ times that due to the forward wave alone, ie $V_F (1 + |\rho|)$. Similarly, when the wave peaks oppose each other, the resultant voltage is only one half of that of the forward wave, ie $V_F (1 - |\rho|)$. The ratio of this maximum to minimum voltage on the line is called the voltage standing wave ratio (VSWR for short, symbol, s). The symbol $|\rho|$ indicates the size of the reflection coefficient, ignoring its associated sign.

Thus

$$s = \frac{1 + |\rho|}{1 - |\rho|}$$

the ratio of the maximum to minimum line voltages.

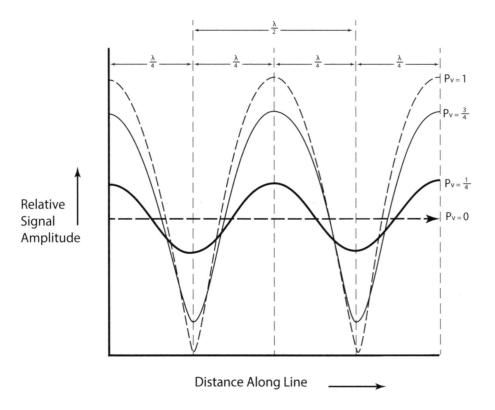

Fig. 4.7 *Amplitude of signals on a line for Various Reflection Coefficients* (ρ)

The actual way in which the voltage in the line varies with distance has been calculated (Appendix C) and is shown in Fig. 4.7 for the cases where $|\rho|$ = 0, ¼, ½, ¾ and 1. Notice that the amplitude of this voltage is not sinusoidal with distance.

Also note that:

$$s = \frac{1 + |\rho|}{1 - |\rho|} \quad \text{for each case.}$$

Summarising then, the presence of reflected waves on a line implies:

1. That the maximum possible power is not delivered to the load - a most important consideration. To achieve this Z_L must be made equal to Z_o.

2. The reflected wave interacts with the forward wave to produce a standing wave where the total voltage on the line varies with the distance along the line. In the case when $|\rho| = 1$ this standing wave will rise to twice the value of the forward wave alone at some positions. Furthermore, if the voltage associated with the forward wave is close to the breakdown voltage of the line, flash-over may occur between the conductors.

3. Additionally, the power losses in both the dielectric between the conductors and the resistance of the conductors themselves, increase significantly.

All of these factors show that the presence of standing waves on a transmission line system is generally undesirable and it is important therefore to minimise them. Ways of achieving this are discussed in the next chapter.

5

Transmission Line Matching

Already outlined in Chapter 4, a wave on a transmission line will eventually encounter the load at its end - usually an antenna. In general, when it arrives at this end, part of the incident wave is absorbed by the load (desirable) and part is reflected back up the line towards the source (undesirable), giving rise to a standing wave on the line. Additionally, less than the maximum possible power is now delivered to the load. The challenge is, therefore, to make an electrical load, whose impedance is not equal to the characteristic impedance of the line, absorb all of the incident wave power. The process of making a load impedance appear to be electrically the same as the characteristic impedance of the line (Z_0) - and therefore absorb all of the incident power - is known as matching.

Again, from Chapter 4, the reflected wave, compared to the incident wave is given by the reflection coefficient of the load, ρ, which is given by

$$\rho = (Z_L - Z_0)/(Z_L + Z_0)$$

Obviously, if Z_L is made electrically equal to Z_0 then $\rho = 0$ and no power is reflected. All of the power in the incident wave is then delivered to the load (antenna).

There are a very large number of ways in which this may be achieved and only some of these are outlined below. As will be deduced from these, at high frequencies the networks tend to use lumped components and at very high frequencies (VHF and above), sections of short-circuited or open-circuited line are used. The general layout, however, is usually as shown in Fig. 5.1 below.

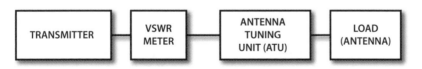

Fig. 5.1 The General Layout

(In practice, the amateur will probably simply adjust the controls of the Antenna Tuning Unit (ATU) until a satisfactory VSWR is achieved - without understanding the operation of the system!).

Matching Using Lumped Components

In general, the terminals of an antenna, or other load, will present an impedance which may be considered to be the equivalent of two electrical components - a resistive component which will appear to dissipate power, which is, in reality, radiated from the antenna and a reactive component which may be considered to be either an inductance or a capacitance. The problem is therefore twofold, a) to remove this reactive part of the impedance and b) to make the remaining resistive part equal to the characteristic impedance of the line (Z_0). Some of the more common methods are described below, but it should be appreciated that this is by no means an exhaustive list. For further reading on this topic (particularly at VHF and UHF) the ARRL's "Antenna Impedance Matching" by WN Caron is particularly recommended.

The L-Section Coupler

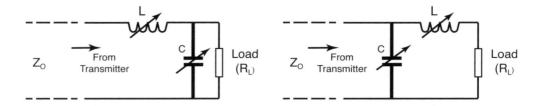

Fig. 5.2 L-Matching Circuits

As will be seen from Fig. 5.2 above, this is probably the simplest of all the matching circuits and the values of the capacitance and inductance can readily be calculated when the impedance of the load is known. It is important to notice that the capacitance must be connected across the higher resistance, of either the load or the characteristic line impedance. It should also be remembered that if the load has any significant inductive or capacitive reactance, this simple matching circuit may not be able to compensate for this and and achieve a satisfactory match. The calculation of the appropriate circuit values is straightforward and is shown, with a worked example, in Appendix D.

The Pi(π) Coupler

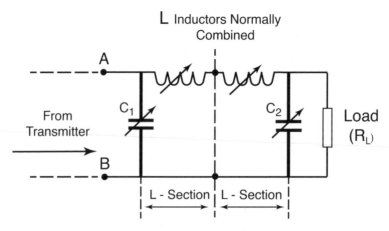

Fig. 5.3 The Pi(π) Section Matching Circuit

The design of the L - section(s) requires some prior knowledge of the resistance of the load, in particular whether it is greater than, or less than, the characteristic impedance of the transmission line. This may be overcome by connecting two such sections together, as shown in Fig. 5.3. As may be expected, the two inductors are normally combined into one component. When properly adjusted, the impedance between A and B in Fig. 5.3 will be resistive and numerically equal to the characteristic impedance of the feeder line. In general, the calculations associated with this operation are quite complex and, unless the actual load impedance is known, the best practical approach is to make successive adjustments to the individual controls until a satisfactory match is indicated by the system's VSWR meter. In practice, the inductor is made variable, either by having a series of switched taps on its windings or by having a "roller-coaster" inductor in which the effective inductance may be varied by moving the position of a mechanical roller, making contact with the coil. The capacitors C_1 and C_2 should be selected to have their vane spacing large enough to withstand the potentially high voltages which may be encountered. It is worth noting that C_2 usually has the higher voltage across it and it should therefore be selected with care.

A range of other configurations is outlined in the RSGB Handbook but even these cannot encompass all of the arrangements likely to be encountered in practice. One point to be appreciated with the π-circuit is its inherent ability to discriminate against any harmonics in the output of the transmitter. The capacitor C_1 will have a reduced reactance at the higher frequencies, tending to short them out, the inductor will have an increased reactance at the higher frequencies, tending to block them off from the antenna (load) and any harmonic power which does get through will again tend to be shorted out by the lowered reactance of C_2.

The T-Circuit

This frequently-encountered circuit is able to match quite a wide range of lines to their loads (antennas) over the majority of the HF bands of interest to radio amateurs. It should be noted that this arrangement requires the two variable capacitors to be ganged together, usually on a common spindle with neither of the capacitors having any connection to the common (earth) line.

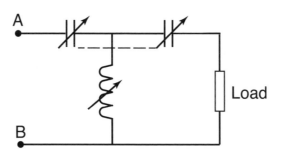

Fig. 5.4 The T-Configuration Matching Circuit

The matching arrangements shown above are all normally suitable for achieving a match between the characteristic impedance of the transmitter's output line and the load over a wide band of frequencies. However, one popular circuit, which does not obviously fall into the T or π configuration is the z-match ATU, shown in Fig. 5.5.

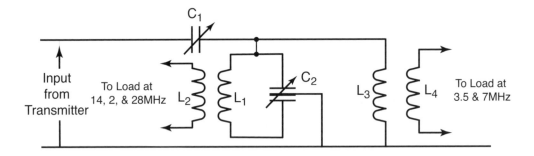

Fig. 5.5 The Z-Match Circuit

There are a few points to note about this circuit:

1. C_1 is normally a 500pF (maximum) variable capacitor (receiving type) but it must be isolated from the common (earth) connection. It is usually adjusted by an insulated extension to it's spindle.

2. C_2 is a split stator capacitor of approximately 250pF (maximum) per section.

3. This tuner has two output connections, each particularly suited to a particular frequency band. Changing the operating band may therefore necessitate the inconvenience of changing the output connection from one output socket to the other.

A more detailed account of this type of ATU, appears in the RSGB's Radio Communication Handbook (p.12.52 et seq.)[1], including information on the two-winding coils and a suggested practical layout.

The Quarter-Wave Transformer

Sometimes the load is a simple resistance (such as a dipole) which may not match the transmission line. In this case the solution is significantly simpler, using the quarter - wave transformer. As is shown in Appendix E, a length of line one quarter of a wavelength long and connected between the feed line and the load will provide a match if the characteristic impedance of this section is made equal to the square root of the product of the resistance of the load and the characteristic impedance of the feeder line, ie:

$$Z_{0\frac{\lambda}{4}} = \sqrt{Z_0 R_L}$$

where $Z_{0\frac{\lambda}{4}}$ and Z_0 are the characteristic impedances of the quarter-wave section and of the feed line respectively and R_L is the resistance of the load. The arrangement is shown on the opposite page for clarity.

If broadband matching is required, then two or more transformers may be connected in series with each other to achieve the desired, broadband matching. If space is not at a premium, then a section of line whose characteristic impedance varies exponentially along its length may, alternatively, be used to realise this broad-band matching - as shown below in Fig. 5.7.

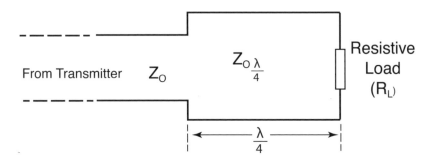

Fig. 5.6 The Quarter-Wave Transformer

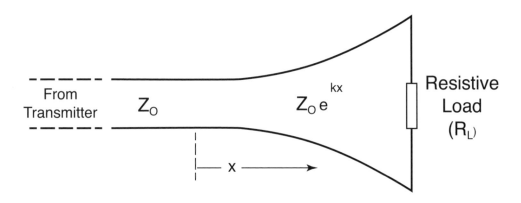

Fig. 5.7 The Exponential Line Transformer

Matching at VHF and UHF Using Stubs

Stubs are simply lengths of transmission line, which may be either short - circuited, or open-circuited at their ends. As is shown in Appendix E, these are simply substitutes for inductors and capacitors respectively and they are especially suitable for use in matching a transmission line to its load at high frequencies (VHF and above). Such stubs are normally connected across the line to be matched, making the adjustment of their positions and/or lengths relatively straightforward (connecting stubs in series with the line can also be used to achieve a match, but installation would imply the cutting of the line - not attractive if an alternative is available). An arbitrarily-chosen load, consisting of a resistance of

122 Ohms in series with a capacitance of reactance 98 Ohms is shown in Fig. 5.8 as an example of the general arrangement. Detailed calculations relating to this example are given in Appendix F.

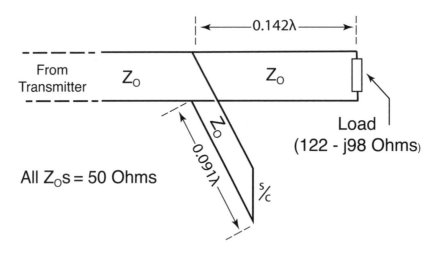

Fig. 5.8 A Typical Stub-Matching Arrangement

References

[1]   RSGB's Radio Communication Handbook (p.12.52 et seq.)
[2]   ARRL's 'Antenna Impedance Matching'

6

Transmission Lines as Resonant Circuit Elements

Appendix E shows the input impedance (Z_S) of a length (x) of line, characteristic imped-ance Z_0 and terminated in a load impedance Z_L to be given by

$$Z_S = (Z_L + jZ_0 \tan \beta x)/(1 + [Z_L/Z_0 \tan \beta x)\ 1.$$

Where β is the phase constant, equal to $2\pi/\lambda$.

If the end of the line is made a short-circuit, then $Z_L = 0$ and equation 1 above be-comes

$$Z_S = jZ_0 \tan \beta x$$

Furthermore, if βx is made equal to $\pi/2$ (ie. 90°), then $x = \lambda/4$ and $Z_S \to \infty$. If βx is less than $\pi/2$ this represents an inductance and if βx is greater than $\pi/2$ (but less than π) it represents a capacitance. This is very similar to the properties of an L-C parallel circuit and, over a small range of frequencies, they may be considered equivalent, as shown in Fig. 6.1 below:

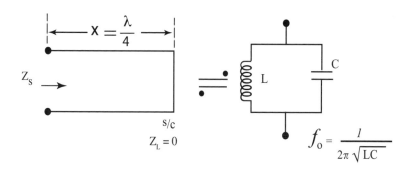

Fig. 6.1 Equivalent Circuits

Similarly, if the line is left open-circuited at its end, then $Z_L = \infty$ and equation 1 above becomes,

$$Z_S = -j\cot \beta x,$$

the terms containing Z_L predominating over all the others. If $\beta x = \pi/2$ then $x = \lambda/4$ and $Z_L \to 0$. If βx is less than $\pi/2$ this represents a capacitance and if βx is greater than $\pi/2$ (but less than π) it represents an inductance. This therefore has the same properties as a series

L-C circuit near resonance and they may therefore be considered equivalent, as indicated in Fig. 6.2.

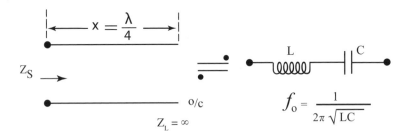

Fig. 6.2 Equivalent Circuits

Using these concepts it is appreciated that these configurations make such line sections readily adaptable to the realisation of filters for use at VHF and UHF. For example, the three-resonant circuit, band pass filter shown in lumped circuit form in Fig. 6.3 is able to be realised using sections of line - as in Fig. 6.4.

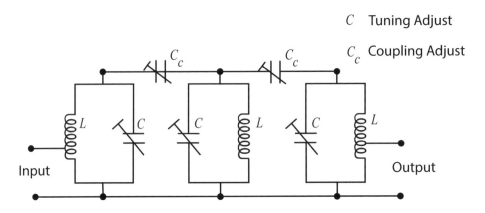

Fig. 6.3 A Lumped-Component, Bandpass Filter

Such filters are often used in amateur repeater systems, where it is important that powerful signals from the transmitter section are kept out of the very sensitive receiver's input. Additionally, it is most desirable that the relatively weak received signals arriving at the receiver's input are not diminished by interaction with the transmitter's output circuits. Such filters are usually manufactured from solid coaxial sections for stability (and are therefore likely to be quite expensive!). If bandstop filters are required, consideration of Equation 1 with $x = \lambda/2$ (ie. $\beta x = 180°$) gives $Z_S = 0$, a short circuit at this frequency. Bandstop filters may therefore be constructed using such $\lambda/2$ sections, in a similar manner to the band pass filters discussed.

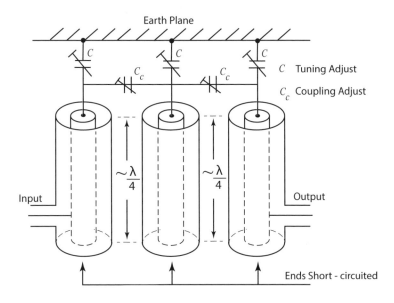

Fig. 6.4 A Coaxial Line Bandpass Filter

Another application where the use of such line sections may be encountered is in the output circuits of high-power VHF and UHF amplifiers. Here the output devices will have a capacitance (to earth). This may be used with a section of line, usually short-circuited at its far end, to form a resonant circuit at the operating frequency. It also provides a convenient, no-signal connection point for the dc feed to the device. For example, the most useful, although now rather dated, Mullard QQV06 - 40A, double - beam power tetrode, has an output capacitance of 2.1pF, which has a reactance of 505 Ohms at 150MHz. A length of transmission line, manufactured from 10mm diameter tubing and spaced at 40mm between conductors, will have a characteristic impedance of 250 Ohms (Appendix B) and, using Equation 6 in Appendix D gives $\beta x = \tan^{-1}(2)$ or $\beta x = 64°$, giving x = 36cm. The overall arrangement is shown below:

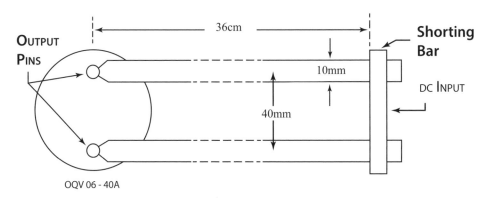

Fig. 6.5 Output Circuit Design

It should be noted that loading this circuit (to extract power) may introduce other components into the circuit which may detune it by a small amount. It is usual to maintain the resonance condition coarsely, by adjusting the position of the short circuit at the end of the line, and to achieve fine tuning by an adjustable metallic vane, arranged to move closer to, or further away from, the line (hence causing small changes in Z_0).

7

Measurements on Transmission Lines

The principal area of measurements which are relevant to transmission systems, are associated with the evaluation of impedances, mainly with a view to achieving a satisfactory match of the line to the load. It is, however, easy to overlook other subsidiary, associated measurements which often have a direct bearing on this problem. Some of these are:

1. The accurate measurement of the frequency of the generator's output, which is always a prime requirement. This is particularly important when wide impedance variations are likely to be encountered over a narrow frequency band - for example some antennas and narrow-band filters. The ideal measuring system would be a digital frequency counter, fed with a very stable reference frequency source such as an oven-controlled crystal oscillator (OCXO), a rubidium source or a source derived from a known, stable transmission, such as the Radio 4 transmission on 198kHz (located at Westerglen) or the France Inter transmission on 162kHz (located at Beaune, Southern France). The frequencies of these transmissions are maintained by reference to atomic sources at the National Physical Laboratory and the French Bureau of Standards respectively. Finally, a further possible, accurate frequency source, now becoming significantly more affordable, is a satellite-controlled oscillator.

2. The voltage on a transmission line may be readily monitored by a simple peak-reading circuit - as indicated in Fig.7.1 below. It should be remembered that the power transmitted, derived from the use of such a measured voltage ($P = V^2/Z_0$) is only true if the line is matched (ie. the load impedance = Z_0).

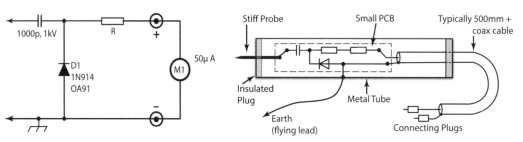

Fig. 7.1 A Simple, Peak-Reading Voltmeter for HF

3. Power flow may be deduced from voltage measurement - as indicated in (2) above - subject to the load being matched to the line. However, a more satisfactory power flow evaluation may be obtained using a directional power meter (such as a Bird through-line wattmeter) or a carefully calibrated VSWR meter, both of which

indicate the forward and reflected powers. The operation of the VSWR meter is outlined in Appendix G. For really high powers, the load is usually a watercooled, resistive element and the power may then be derived from thermal considerations.

The Measurement of Impedance (or Admittance)

These measurements generally fall into two areas, bridges for use at high frequencies and line voltage or current measurements for VHF and above, although there is a good deal of overlap between the two.

Bridge Measurements

There are a wide variety of bridge configurations available to measure both impedance and admittance and an excellent summary may be found in the rather dated, Royal Signals Handbook of Line Communication, Volume 1, pp.272/274. Care should be taken in the construction of these bridges to keep all the leads as short as possible and to ensure that the arrangement is well screened. An additional problem arises from the use of resistors in some arms of these bridges. Conventional resistors, which work well at low frequencies, are likely to become very reactive at high frequencies and this will then give rise to significant measurement errors.

The most useful bridge for radio amateur use is without doubt the Wheatstone bridge, two versions of which are shown in Figs. 7.2 and 7.3.

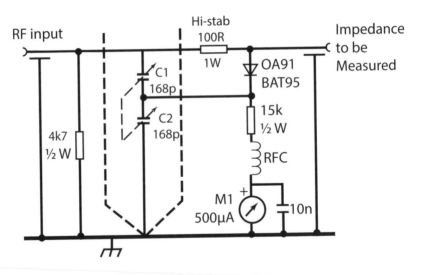

Fig. 7.2 A Simple RF Bridge

With both these circuits, balance is achieved when the input impedance of the line is resistive. In the simple RF bridge circuit, balance is obtained when the input resistance to the line (r) is given by

$$r = 100 \; C1/C2$$

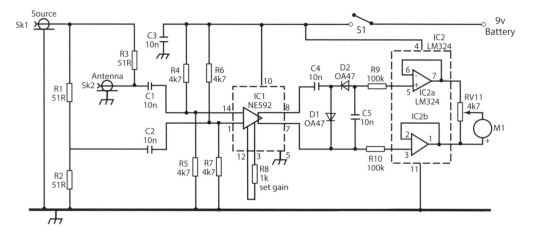

Fig. 7.3 An Amplified RF Bridge

Note that the 100 Ohm, high-stability resistor, in Fig 7.2 should be a carbon composition (ie low reactance), component and that C1 and C2 should be arranged so that as one is increased in value, so the other is decreased in value. In the second circuit, balance is achieved when the antenna's impedance is 51 Ohms and resistive. If the characteristic impedance of the line is 50 (or 51) Ohms, then the load is matched to the line under balance conditions.

General Impedance Measurements on Line Systems

Commercially, transmission line measurements are most frequently carried out using a network analyser. This equipment is able to give a direct reading of the reflection coefficient of the load, usually using S-parameters. The use of the slotted line has largely been superceded by the network analyser but, in practice, they may be occasionally encountered. The Smith Chart may be useful in the application of the results obtained from either of these sources and a copy appears as Appendix F for completeness.

References

[1] Royal Signals Handbook of Line Communication, Volume 1, pp.278/279

[2] Clive Smith's "Test Equipment for the Radio Amateur", p.126. (RSGB)

Appendix A

Some Other Wave Guiding Systems

The Microstrip Line

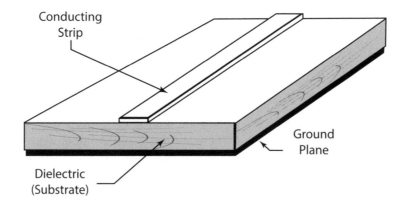

This system is often encountered in microwave components. Potential users are referred to the excellent and comprehensive book by: T.C. Edwards and M.B. Steer, "Foundations of Interconnect and Microstrip Design" (3rd edition) Pub: Wiley & Sons, ISBN: 9780 4716 0701 4

The Triplate Line

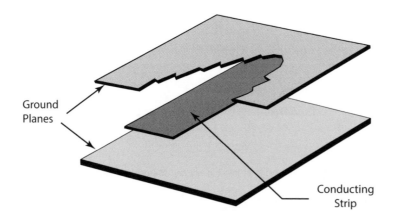

The Rectangular Waveguide

Here the wavelength of the energy is not simply related to the frequency, but involves the broad dimension of the waveguide - as indicated by the relationship:

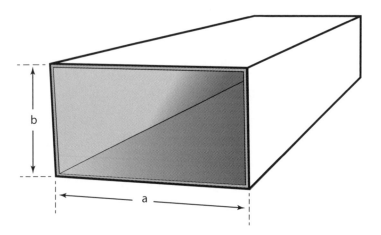

$$1/(\lambda_g)^2 = 1/(\lambda_0)^2 - 1/(2a)^2$$

where λ_g is the wavelength within the waveguide, λ_0 is the free space wavelength and a is the broad dimension of the waveguide. There are many excellent books on this subject - for reference I used this book, 'Services Textbook of Radio', Volume 5 which contains first class drawings of waves in waveguides as well as a good exposition of the nature of the waves themselves.

References

[1]   T.C. Edwards and M.B. Steer, "Foundations of Interconnect and Microstrip Design"   (3rd edition)Pub: Wiley & Sons, ISBN: 9780 4716 0701 4

[2]   "Services Textbook of Radio", Volume 5 (1958)

Appendix B

Some Characteristics of Open Twin and Coaxial Line Systems

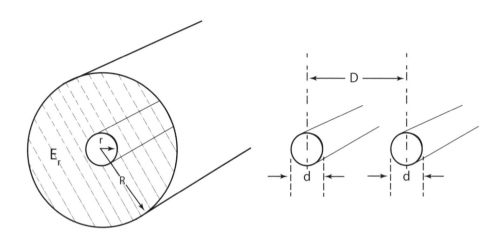

Coaxial Line	**Open Twin feeder**
Inductance = $0.46\log_{10}(R/r)$ µH/m	Inductance = $0.921\log_{10}(2D/d)$ µH/m
Capacitance = $24.1\varepsilon_r/\log_{10}(R/r)$ pF/m	Capacitance = $12.05\varepsilon_r/\log_{10}(2D/d)$ pF/m
$Z_0 = 138\log_{10}(R/r)$ Ohms	$Z_0 = 276\log_{10}(2D/d)$ Ohms

where ε_r is the relative dielectric constant of the material between the conductors.

Appendix C

Voltages on a Transmission Line With Standing Waves

In general there will be two waves present on a transmission line, the forward wave, represented by $V_F \sin(\omega t - \beta x)$ and the reverse wave, represented by $V_R \sin(\omega t + \beta x)$ where ω is the angular frequency $(2\pi f)$, β is the phase constant $(2\pi/\lambda)$ and x is the distance along the line. The actual size of the reflected wave (V_R) is determined by the reflection coefficient (ρ) of the load. Hence we may write $V_R = \rho V_F$ and the total voltage on the line is given by

$$v = V_F\{\sin(\omega t - \beta x) + \rho\sin(\omega t + \beta x)\}$$

Expanding this gives

$$v = V_F\{\sin\omega t.\cos\beta x - \cos\omega t.\sin\beta x + \rho(\sin\omega t.\cos\beta x + \cos\omega t.\sin\beta x)\}$$

or

$$v = V_F\{[(1 + \rho)\cos\beta x]\sin\omega t - [(1 - \rho)\sin\beta x]\cos\omega t\}$$

Rewriting this in the form $A.\sin(\omega t + \varphi)$ shows, after some manipulation, that

$$A = V_F \sqrt{(1 + \rho)^2 + 4\rho\cos^2\beta x}$$

The phase φ is not usually of interest here but may be obtained by trigonometric manipulation of the equation for v. For the purposes of simplicity, the reflection coefficient ρ has been assumed to be entirely real. In practice, with reactive loads, ρ will be complex, although the final results will be identical to the situations indicated in Chapter 4, but the initial phase of the reflected wave will be modified.

Appendix D

The Design of L-Match Circuits

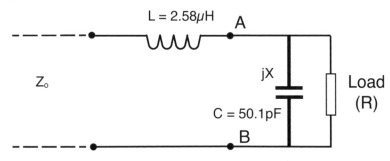

Fig. 5.1 An L-Match Circuit

The impedance (z) to the right of points A and B in the above circuit is given by

$$Z = \frac{jRX}{R+jX} = \frac{jRX(R-jX)}{R^2+X^2} = \frac{R(X^2+jRX)}{R^2+X^2}$$

The real part of this impedance is $\frac{RX^2}{R^2+X^2}$ This is obviously less than R, and if
the reactive 'j' terms can be cancelled out a match may be achieved to Z_0 (providing it is
less than R). The reactive term, $\frac{R^2X}{R^2+X^2}$ may be cancelled by a series reactance.
of opposite sign. As an example, consider the design of a 14MHz matching section,
terminated in a load of 600 Ohms, which is to be matched to a line whose characteristic
impedance is 75 Ohms. Substituting, using the above expressions:

$$Z_0 = \frac{RX^2}{R^2+X^2} = 75 = \frac{600\,X^2}{(600)^2+X^2}$$

then

$$75(600)^2 + 75X^2 = 600X^2$$

$$525X^2 = 75(600)^2$$

and

$$X = 600\sqrt{\frac{75}{525}} = 227 \text{ Ohms.}$$

If this is a capacitance then

$$\frac{1}{\omega C} = 227 \quad C = \frac{1}{227.\, 2\pi 14.10^6} \qquad C = 50.1\text{pF}.$$

Therefore $\omega L = 227$ Ohms and $L = \dfrac{227}{2\pi 14.10^6}$ H. $= 2.58\mu$H.

If the load contains a parallel capacitance of more than 50.1pF, matching will not be able to be achieved using this circuit.

In the event that the reverse problem is encountered - to match a 75 Ohm load to a 600 Ohm line, the solution would yield the same component values, but with the capacitor connected across the line and result in the circuit shown in Fig. 5.2 below:

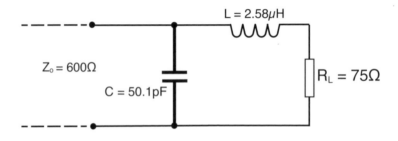

Fig. 5.1.2 L-Match Circuit.

Summarising this procedure:

If $R > Z_0$ then

$$C = \frac{1}{\omega R} \sqrt{\frac{R - Z_0}{Z_0}}$$

and $L = \dfrac{R}{\omega} \sqrt{\dfrac{Z_0}{R - Z_0}}$

and if $R < Z_0$ then

$$C = \frac{1}{\omega Z_0} \sqrt{\frac{Z_0 - R}{R}}$$

and $\qquad L = \dfrac{Z_0}{\omega} \sqrt{\dfrac{R}{Z_0 - R}}$

Appendix E

Voltages and Currents on a Loss-Free Transmission Line

Some Important Results

It may be shown that the voltage and current on a transmission line are given by:

$$V_S = V_R \cos \beta x + jI_R Z_0 \sin \beta x$$

and

$$I_S = I_R \cos \beta x + j(V_R/Z_0) \sin \beta x$$

where V_S and I_S are the voltage and current at the sending end of the line, V_R and I_R are the voltage and current at the receiving end of the line, β is the phase constant $(2\pi/\lambda)$, Z_0 is the line's characteristic impedance and x is the length of the line. Hence the input impedance at the sending end $(Z_S = V_S/I_S)$ is:

$$Z_S = (V_R \cos \beta x + jI_R Z_0 \sin \beta x)/(I_R \cos \beta x + j[V_R/Z_0] \sin \beta x)$$

Dividing both the numerator and denominator by $I_R \cos \beta x$ and replacing V_R/I_R with Z_L, the load impedance gives

$$Z_S = (Z_L + jZ_0 \tan \beta x)/(1 + j[Z_L/Z_0] \tan \beta x)\text{.. ....} \quad 1.$$

Alternatively, the input admittance $(Y_S = I_S/V_S)$ may be calculated from these first two equations as

$$Y_S = (Y_L + jY_0 \tan \beta x)/(1 + j[Y_L/Y_0] \tan \beta x)\text{...... ....} \quad 2.$$

The Quarter-Wave Transformer

If $x = \lambda/4$. The tangent terms predominate in equation 1 above, and

$$Z_S = Z_0^2/Z_L \text{ or } Z_0 = \sqrt{Z_S Z_L}\text{.... ....} \quad 3.$$

Open-Circuited Stubs

If a line is open - circuit at its end, Z_L is now infinite. Only those terms in equation 1 which contain Z_L, are then relevant and

$$Z_S = -jZ_0 \cot \beta x\text{. ....} \quad 4.$$

If $\beta x < \pi/2$ (ie. $< 90°$) then this represents a capacitance which may be used in the matching process at VHF and above.

Alternatively, this may be expressed as a susceptance using equation 2 above:

$$Y_S = jY_0 \cot \beta x \; .... \; 5.$$

- again a capacitance.

Short-Circuited Stubs

Similarly, if a length of line is short-circuited at its end, $Z_L = 0$ and equation 1 becomes

$$Z_S = jZ_0 \tan \beta x \; .... \; 6.$$

Again, providing $\beta x < \pi/2$ (ie. $< 90°$) this represents an inductance which may also be used in the matching process at high frequencies. As with the short-circuit stub above, this may alternatively be represented by a susceptance using equation 2 above as:

$$Y_S = -jY_0 \cot \beta x \; .... \; 7.$$

Inverting Quarter-Wave Sections

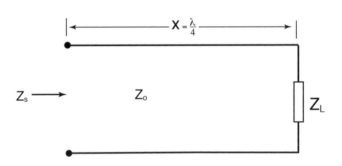

Fig. 5.2.1 The Quarter-Wave Line

From equation 1, if βx is made equal to $\pi/2$ (90°), corresponding to a line of length $\lambda/4$, then the tangent terms in both the numerator and denominator predominate and the whole expression becomes:

$$Z_S = Z_0^2/Z_L$$

or

$$Z_S/Z_0 = 1/(Z_L/Z_0)$$

ie. the load impedance, expressed as a fraction of the characteristic impedance of the line is inverted. This is now the same as the load's admittance, compared to the characteristic admittance of the line (Y_L/Y_0) - a useful result when considering matching systems using shunt stubs, as in the example given at the end of Chapter 5.

Appendix F

Solution to a Matching Problem

As discussed in Chapter 5, the example problem to be solved is to match an impedance of 122 - j98 Ohms to a 50 Ohm line, using a shunt stub, placed at an appropriate position across the line - repeated below for clarity.

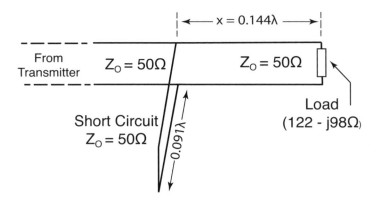

Fig. 5.3.1 Matching Example

Solution by Calculation.

From Appendix D, it is shown that:

$$Y_S = I_S/V_S = (Y_L + jY_0 \tan \beta x)/(1 + j[Y_L/Y_0]\tan \beta x).$$

The admittance of the load is calculated as:

$$Y_L = 1/Z_L = 1/(122 - j98) = (4.98 + j4.00)10^{-3} \text{ S}.$$

Substituting this value of Y_L, with $Y_0 = 1/Z_0 = 1/50 = 20.10^{-3}$ S yields a complex fractional expression for Y_S, and after rationalisation, the real part should be made equal to Y_0.

The solution of this equation then gives:

$$\tan\beta x = \tan(2\pi x/\lambda) = 1.278$$

or

$$x = 0.143\lambda$$

The susceptive part of Y_S/Y_0 may now be calculated as j1.56 and a shunt stub, short-circuited at its end and whose characteristic impedance is 50 Ohms so that $\cot\beta x = 1.56$ will achieve a match.

This gives a stub length of 0.098λ.

Solution Using the Smith Chart

The rather tedious calculations over page may be conveniently circumvented using this chart (on page 47) and the thumbnail sketches below which indicate the steps involved to solve this problem.

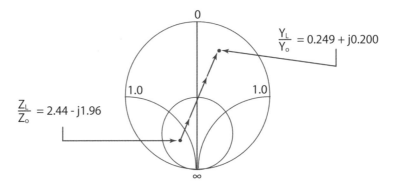

a) Transformation of the load impedance (Z_L/Z_0) to its equivalent susceptance (Y_L/Y_0).

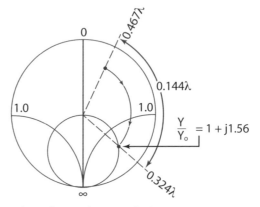

b) Location of position on the line where the conductance is 1.

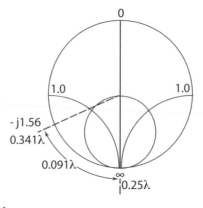

c) Evaluation of stub length.

Fig. 5.3.2 Smith Chart of the Matching Example's Solution

The Smith Chart

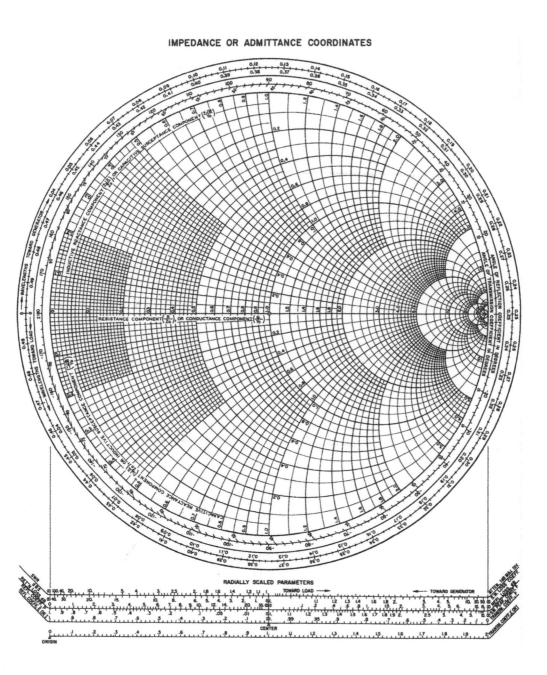

IMPEDANCE OR ADMITTANCE COORDINATES

Reproduced from ARRL Handbook

Appendix G
The VSWR Meter

reproduced from RadCom articles published in May 2012 and Nov 2013

Frequently Seen Item

The most common measuring instrument in the average amateur's shack is probably the multimeter. This may be either an analogue instrument – the moving coil meter – or it may use digital techniques to measure a range of electrical parameters. The operation of these most important instruments is readily understood by their users and normally presents no difficulty in appreciating the wide variety of their uses.

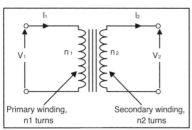

Primary winding, n1 turns   Secondary winding, n2 turns

Fig 7.1.1 Voltages and currents in a transformer

The next in line for popularity is probably the SWR meter, used to detect the presence of waves reflected from a transmitter's load (usually the antenna). The operation of this meter is not usually so well understood by amateurs, although some attempts in current publications do give very sketchy outlines of its action (notably the RSGB Handbook and Moxon's Antennas for all Locations). It was therefore decided to look more closely at the operation of this most useful device in order to understand its operating principles and also to appreciate some of its inherent limitations.

Preliminary Points

There are three, straightforward points to appreciate before we are able to fully understand the operation of the SWR meter: the transformer, waves on the transmission line and Ohm's law. We will look at these in turn.

The Transformer

Most amateurs will be familiar with the operation of the transformer and its use to step up, or to step down, alternating voltages. The primary and secondary voltages (V_1 and V_2 in Fig. 7.1.1) are directly related to the number of turns on each winding, ie

$$\frac{V_2}{V_1} = \frac{n_2}{n_1}$$

Additionally (and more relevantly in the context of the SWR meter) the primary and secondary currents are related by:

$$\frac{I_2}{I_1} = \frac{n_1}{n_2}$$

Hence, if the voltage is reduced, by making n_2 smaller than n_1, the current will be increased by the same amount – and vice versa.

Waves on the Transmission Line

If a signal generator (transmitter) is connected to one end of a transmission line, usually
either a coaxial cable or an open twin feeder, then an electromagnetic wave will travel down the line at somewhat less than the
speed of light, as shown in Fig. 7.1.2. This
wave, known as the forward wave, will trav-

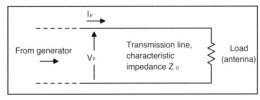

*Fig. 7.1.2 Forward voltage and current waves,
travelling from a generator to its load*

el down the line towards the load as a voltage (V_F) and an associated current (I_F). The
ratio of this voltage to the current is the same everywhere on the line, irrespective of any
other voltages or currents that may be pres-
ent, and is fixed by the geometry of the line.
This is known as the characteristic impedance of the line (symbol Z_0).

Thus $\quad \dfrac{V_F}{I_F} = Z_0$

When the forward wave arrives at the load,
the energy is generally split into two parts
– some is absorbed by the load at the line's
end (usually the antenna) and some is reflected back up the line, towards the generator – as indicated in Fig. 7.1.3. Again, the
voltage and current of the reflected wave
(VR and IR respectively) are related by

$$\dfrac{V_R}{I_R} = Z_0,$$

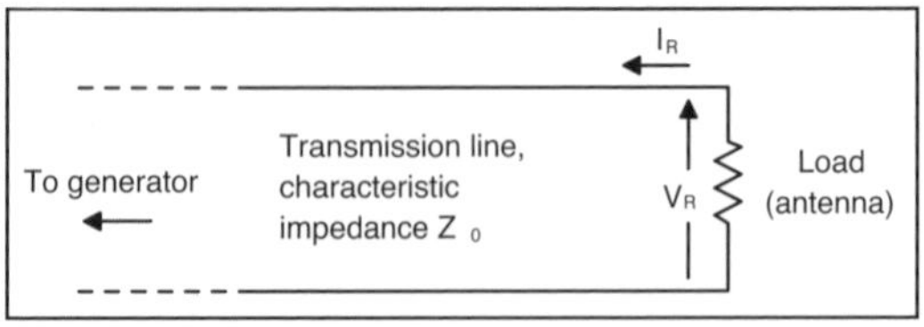

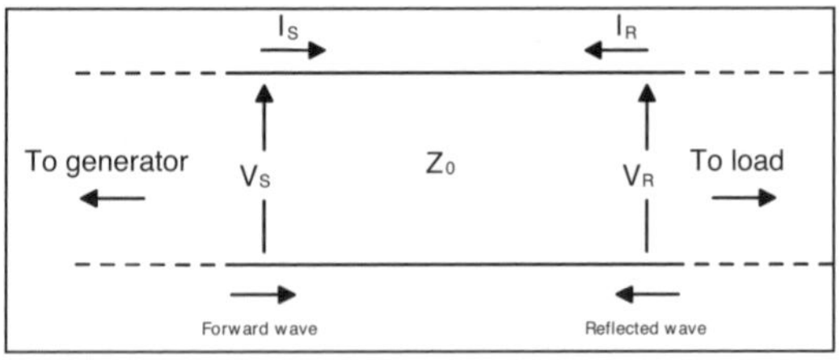

*Fig. 7.1.3 Reverse (reflected) voltage and current
waves, travelling from a load to the generator*

*Fig. 7.1.4 A transmission line with both forward and
reverse waves present*

the characteristic impedance of the line, in a similar manner to the forward wave already
discussed. Note especially, that the reflected current in this wave is travelling in the opposite direction to the current in the forward wave. In general then, there will be two waves
present on a line connecting a generator to a load – the forward wave, travelling towards
the load and a reflected wave, travelling back towards the generator, as in Fig. 7.1.4.

Thus, at any point on the line, there will be two waves present, travelling in opposite directions to each other. It is the combination of these two waves which gives rise to a standing
wave – of which, more later.

The voltages associated with these waves at any point on the line will simply add to each
other, but the currents will subtract from each other, as they are travelling in opposite directions. The voltage at any point will therefore be $V_F + VR$ but the currents will be IF – IR
(assuming the reflected wave to be smaller than the forward wave).

Ohm's Law

To understand the action of the SWR meter, a reminder of the voltage/current relationship conventions was thought worthwhile:

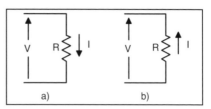

In Fig. 7.1.5 a), it will be appreciated that the voltage (V) and the current (I) are related by $V = IR$, Ohm's law. Notice that the convention is for the current to flow from the 'head' of the voltage arrow to its 'tail'.

Fig. 7.1.5 Conventions used in Ohm's Law (see text)

If the current is shown to flow from the 'tail' of the voltage arrow, as in Fig. 7.1.5 b), then $V = -IR$.

With these three straightforward points made, we are now in a position to understand the working of the VSWR meter.

The VSWR Meter

The transmission line, shown in Fig. 7.1.6 as a coaxial cable, is passed through the hole of a high permeability ferrite toroid. This conductor acts as the single turn primary of a transformer, carrying a current $I_F - I_R$ (the combined currents of the forward and reverse waves). The current, $I2$, in the n_2-turn secondary is therefore

$$I_2 = \frac{I_F - I_R}{n_2}$$

The voltages V_1 and V_2 are

$$V_1 = \frac{Z_0 I_2}{2} = \frac{Z_0 (I_F - I_R)}{2n_2}$$

and

$$V_2 = \frac{-Z_0 I_2}{2} = \frac{-Z_0 (I_F - I_R)}{2n_2}$$

Or, putting $I_F = \dfrac{V_F}{Z_0}$ and $I_R = \dfrac{V_R}{Z_0}$

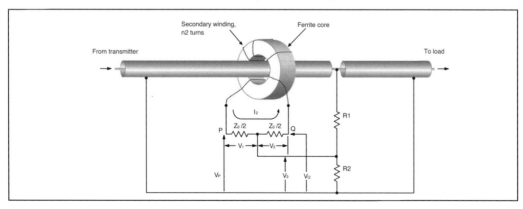

Fig. 7.1.6 VSWR meter outline circuit

these become

$$V_1 = \frac{V_F - V_R}{2n_2} \quad \text{and} \quad V_2 = \frac{-(V_F - V_R)}{2n_2}$$

Transferring our attention to R1 and R2 on the right hand side of the diagram, the voltage across the two resistors is $V_F + V_R$. The current through R1 and R2 is

$$\frac{V_F + V_R}{R1 + R2}$$

and the voltage, V3, across R2 is

$$\frac{R2\,(V_F + V_R)}{R1 + R2}$$

– a potential divider.

The voltage at point P in the diagram is therefore

$$V_P = V_3 + V_1 = \frac{R2\,(V_F + V_R)}{R1 + R2} + \frac{V_F - V_R}{2n_2}$$

and at point Q is

$$V_Q = V_3 + V_2 = \frac{R2\,(V_F + V_R)}{R1 + R2} - \frac{V_F - V_R}{2n_2}$$

if $\dfrac{R2}{R1 + R2}$ is made equal to $\dfrac{1}{2n_2}$

then these become

$$V_P = \frac{V_F}{n_2} \text{ and } V_Q = \frac{V_R}{n_2}$$

– voltages proportional to the forward wave, and to the reverse wave: success!

As V_P and V_Q are alternating voltages, it is usual to connect a simple diode rectifier arrangement to both points P and Q to produce DC outputs representing the peak values of V_P and V_Q which may then be measured by DC voltmeters.

A typical, practical description of the construction of this instrument may be found in the *Test Equipment for the Radio Amateur*, from which Fig. 7.1.7 is reproduced for completeness.

Some interesting deductions may be made from this circuit:

1) The value of RV1 in parallel with R2 should be such that

$$\frac{1}{2n_2} = \frac{R2}{R1 + R2} = \frac{1}{2 \cdot 12}$$

This gives R2 as 217Ω, including the 1k in parallel. The setting for RV1 should therefore be about 489Ω – about one half of the 1k track available. This is normally adjusted on test using a known good dummy load.

2) The power lost within the instrument is essentially the power lost in the voltage sampling resistors R1, R2 and RV1 plus the power dissipated in R3 and R4. If the load is matched to the line, only the forward wave's voltage and current are present and taking a 100W power flow down the line (and taking Z_0 to be 50Ω) gives $V_F = 70.7V$ and $I_F = 1.41A$.

The power taken from the wave in both the voltage sampling resistors and the two resistors, totaling 50Ω, is readily calculated as 1.7W – a negligible fraction of the 100W in the forward wave.

Variations on the Theme.

In practice, one may encounter several variations on the basic circuit. The resistor chain consisting of R1, R2 and RV1 may be replaced by a capacitive voltage dividing arrangement. Although this appears to eliminate the power losses in the resistive dividing system shown here, a resistor is necessary to complete a DC path for the divider and the meter currents. This does, obviously consume some power.

Some circuits replace the resistor chain shown here with another transformer, identical with T1 in Fig. 7. In this case the 12 turn winding would be placed across the line and the one turn secondary would be connected to the junction of the two 27Ω resistors and the common (earth) rail. The transformer T1 may also appear as a pair of closely coupled printed lines, the operation of which is outside the scope of this article, but could be made the subject of a future contribution.

Shortcomings and Points to Note

For the circuit to work correctly, all resistors must actually be resistors at the frequencies concerned. Most resistors are quite reactive at high frequencies. Carbon composition components are traditionally used in this instrument as they are generally recognised to be the least reactive type of component.

The connection of R1 to the line should, ideally, be made precisely where it passes through the hole in the toroid, T1. In practice, the connection will be made to one or other side of this optimum point and some small error will inevitably result.

Calibration.

There is no real substitute for calibrating this instrument against a known, accurate meter, such as the Bird through line wattmeter. Fortunately, further analysis of the circuit gives us a good ballpark figure for the voltage wave, the associated current wave and the power travelling in each direction on the line.

The voltages at points P and Q in Fig. 7.1.6 have been shown to be

$$\frac{V_F}{n_2} \text{ and } \frac{V_R}{n_2} \text{ respectively}$$

assuming VR1 to have been correctly adjusted using a known good 50Ω load. Referring back to the complete circuit (Fig. 7.1.7), it will be noted that these signal voltages are rectified by the diodes D1 and D2 and, in conjunction with the capacitors C1 and C2 providing a peak indication of VP and VQ. Thus

$$V_P(pk) = \frac{\sqrt{2} V_F}{n_2} \text{ and } V_Q(pk) = \frac{\sqrt{2} V_R}{n_2}$$

Here the forward voltage drops in D1 and D2 have been neglected but, if desired, may be assumed to be in the range 0.5 to 1.0V and the appropriate corrections made.

As an example, if the range switch is set to, say, the 50W FSD position then the current in the meter will be

$$\frac{\sqrt{2} V_F}{n_2} . 10^{-5} A$$

(neglecting the internal resistance of the meter – typically around 5k for a moving coil instrument). For 50W travelling down the line, the forward voltage on the line will be

$$V_F = \sqrt{P \cdot Z_0} = \sqrt{50 \cdot 50} = 50V \text{ (RMS)}$$

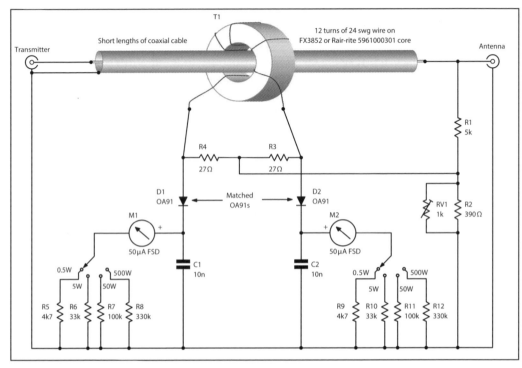

Fig. 7.1.7 The VSWR circuit

The meter current is then

$$\frac{\sqrt{2 \cdot 50}}{12 \cdot 10^5} A = 60\mu A$$

– on the high side, but this would be reduced to nearer 50µA by making allowances for the diode voltage drop, the internal resistance of the meter and R3 and R4 being slightly higher than one half of the 50Ω characteristic impedance of the line. Identical considerations apply to the section used to evaluate the parameters of the reflected wave.

Measuring VSWR

The voltage standing wave ratio (VSWR) may also be obtained from VF and VR:

$$\frac{V_F + V_R}{V_F - V_R} = \frac{I_F R_F + I_R R_R}{I_F R_F - I_R R_R}$$

where I_F and I_R are the currents indicated on the meters measuring the forward and reverse wave respectively and R_F and R_R are the corresponding resistors (usually the same) switched in series with the meters. In some VSWR meters, using two meters in a common casing and arranged so the needles cross enables the VSWR to be obtained from a scale engraved on the meter's face.

If V_P and V_Q are input via an analogue to digital converter to a microprocessor, the device can calculate and display forward and reverse power levels and the reflection coefficient of the load, making a very versatile instrument.

How the tandem match works

An alternative circuit arrangement, using two identical toroids, known variously as the Stockton circuit, the tandem match or the four port hybrid transformer. The circuit of this arrangement, reproduced from *Clive Smith's Test Equipment for the Radio Amateur*, is shown in Fig. 7.1.8.

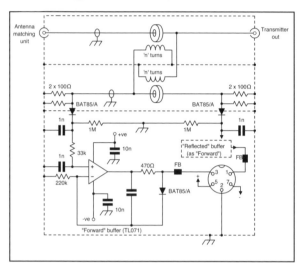

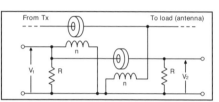

Fig. 7.1.9 Skeleton circuit of the tandem match

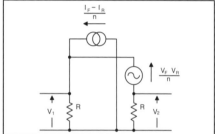

Fig. 7.1.8 The 'Tandem Match' VSWR circuit

Fig. 7.1.10 Simplified skeleton circuit for analysis

Circuit Operation

As may be expected, the heart of this system lies in the action of the two transformers and their associated 50Ω resistors (two 100Ω resistors in parallel in the diagram). To analyse this, the circuit has been simplified to include only those components relevant to its basic action, shown in Fig. 7.1.9.

To recapitulate from the first article on this subject, the current on the main feeder passing through the upper toroid and constituting one effective turn is $I_F - I_R$, where I_F is the current associated with the forward wave, travelling from the transmitter to the load and I_R is the current associated with he reflected wave, travelling back from the load towards the transmitter. If the number of turns on the secondary of this toroid is 'n', then the current in the secondary is $(I_F - I_R)/n$.

The lower, identical toroid is essentially a voltage-reducing transformer, fed from the main feeder where the voltage is $V_F + V_R$, the sum of the voltages associated with the forward and reverse wave respectively. The voltage induced in the single turn, passing through the central hole, is therefore $(V_F + V_R)/n$. Using these thoughts, the circuit may be simplified to its skeleton form, shown in Fig. 7.1.10.

To determine V_1 and V_2 the superposition theorem is used: first analyse the circuit with the current generator suppressed (ie replaced by an open circuit), then analyse again with the voltage generator suppressed (ie replaced with an open circuit). The actual voltages

V_1 and V_2 are then the sum of the contributions of each generator. Suppressing the current generator yields the circuit shown in Fig. 7.1.11.

This gives $V_A = (V_F + V_R)/2n$ and $V_B = -(V_F + V_R)/2n$

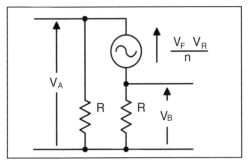

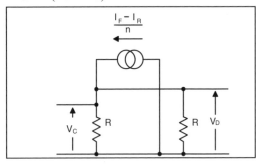

Fig. 7.1.11 Fig. 7.1.10 with current generator suppressed

Fig. 7.1.12 Fig.7.1.10 with voltage generator suppressed

Similarly, suppressing the voltage source to zero and replacing it with a short circuit reduces Fig. 7.1.10 to the arrangement shown in Fig. 7.1.12.

This gives $V_C = V_D = R(I_F - I_R)/2n$

and since $I_F = V_F/Z_0$ and $I_R = V_R/Z_0$ these become

$V_C = V_D = R(V_F - V_R)/2nZ_0$

Provided $R = Z_0$ this becomes $V_C = V_D = (V_F - V_R)/2n$

Adding these voltages gives

$V_1 = V_A + V_C = (V_F + V_R)/2n + (V_F - V_R)/2n = V_F/n$

and $V_2 = V_B + V_D = - (V_F + V_R)/2n + (V_F - V_R)/2n = - V_R/n$

Thus V1 represents the voltage associated with the forward wave and V_2 the voltage associated with the reflected wave, each simply scaled down by the turns ratio n. It will be appreciated that these are alternating voltages which are usually rectified and smoothed to produce a DC voltage that corresponds to their peak values.

As an example, taking a fairly typical value of 10 for n and assuming a transmitter supplying a forward power of 100W in a 50Ω line gives a peak line voltage of 100V. The rectified forward indication will therefore be 100/10 V = 10V – a reasonable voltage that is large enough to swamp any potentially serious inaccuracies due to rectifier drops etc.

Finally, it must be noted that the 50Ω resistors in this circuit must be chosen to be equal in value to the characteristic impedance of the line if correct readings are to be obtained – a constraint not present in the earlier, single transformer circuit. It is also recommended that these components are selected with care: carbon film types are now available with excellent HF characteristics – although they are rather expensive!

References

[1] RSGB Handbook and Test Equipment for the Radio Amateur, from which Fig. 7.1.7 is reproduced

[2] RSGB Handbook

[3] Moxon's Antennas for all Locations

References

RSGB's Radio Communication Handbook

Antenna Impedance Matching" by WN Caron

Royal Signals Handbook of Line Communication, Volume 1

Clive Smith's "Test Equipment for the Radio Amateur" (RSGB)

T.C. Edwards and M.B. Steer, "Foundations of Interconnect and Microstrip Design" (3rd edition) Pub: Wiley & Sons, ISBN: 9780 4716 0701 4

Services Textbook of Radio, Volume 5

RSGB Handbook and Test Equipment for the Radio Amateur, from which Fig. 7.1.7 is reproduced

Moxon's Antennas for all Locations

Appendix G These pages on the VSWR Meter first appeared in the RSGB RadCom magazine in the May 2012 and Nov 2013 editions

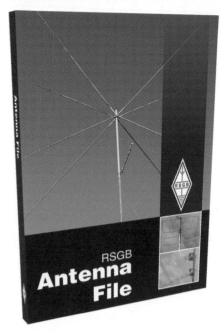

RSGB Antenna File

The Radio Society of Great Britain (RSGB) has been promoting antenna experimentation for over 100 years and for most of this time publishing the work done in its monthly journal. The RSGB Journal *RadCom* has therefore developed a reputation for producing some of the best material on antennas published anywhere. This book is a compilation of some of the best articles about antennas that have been published in the RSGB in recent years.

The *RSGB Antenna File* covers all parts of the spectrum from HF to UHF - and even LF and microwave frequencies. From simple wire dipoles to more complex multi-band and multi-element arrays, *RSGB Antenna File* contains dozens of 'how to' constructional articles, complemented by many features explaining how antennas work, facts about feed lines, antenna matching, earthing and much more besides. The doublet, Moxon and 'Super Moxon', cubical quad, 'low noise' and 'long' Yagis, log periodic, loaded dipole, horizontal loop, magnetic loop, delta loop and J-pole are just some of the antenna designs featured in this book.

The *RSGB Antenna File* reproduces the articles as originally published and is broken down into five logical sections. *HF Antennas* is the first and largest section and this is followed by a section covering *VHF, UHF and Microwave Antennas*. Antenna experimentation is though much more than this, so readers will also find sections on *Feeders and Baluns* and *ATUs and Antenna Matching*. There is even a section of the less easily defined antenna article called *Miscellaneous Antenna Articles*.

In short, there are nearly 120 antenna articles here crammed into 288 pages with information on antennas of all types that will be of interest to all antenna experimenters everywhere. Today antenna experimentation is alive and well and as popular as ever, making the *RSGB Antenna File* a 'must have' book for every radio amateur.

Size 210x297mm, 288pages, ISBN: 9781 9050 8687 0

RRP £14.99

Radio Society of Great Britain **www.rsgbshop.org**

3 Abbey Court, Priory Business Park, Bedford, MK44 3WH. Tel: 01234 832 700 Fax: 01234 831 496

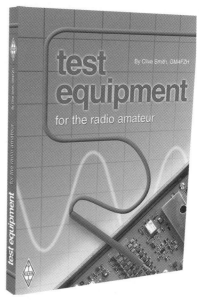

Test Equipment for the Radio Amateur
4th Edition

By Clive Smith, GM4FZH

Many of us would like to analyse the performance of our stations but find that professional test equipment such as spectrum analysers prohibitively expensive. Yet it can be easy to make many pieces of very useful test equipment yourself at home. *Test Equipment for the Radio Amateur* is a book that provides the definitive guide to the equipment that can be made or used to measure the various parameters of an amateur radio station.

This fourth edition of *Test Equipment for the Radio Amateur* has been fully updated to show what can be achieved today with the simple, inexpensive and easily obtainable. Test equipment for measuring current, voltage, the value of components, frequencies, receiver performance, RF power, modulation, antennas and transmission lines, noise, transmitter linearity and much more is all covered. For the home builder there are numerous projects, from a simple fuse tester to a high quality 1.3GHz signal source and much more. One chapter even covers software based test equipment that runs on a PC and includes specialist calculators, oscilloscope and spectrum analyser programs, signal generators, SINAD analysis and even design tools for RF filters. Surplus equipment often appears on the amateur market and the use of this equipment such as frequency counters and oscilloscopes, is well documented in this book. There is an appendix of useful reference data with everything from resistor colour coding to discrete semiconductor coding and surface mount device identification to common coaxial cable equivalents. There is even a second appendix of PCB and component layout diagrams for many of these projects.

Size 174x240mm, 256 pages, ISBN: 9781 9050 8672 6

RRP £14.99

Radio Society of Great Britain **www.rsgbshop.org**

3 Abbey Court, Priory Business Park, Bedford, MK44 3WH. Tel: 01234 832 700 Fax: 01234 831 496

RSGB *shop*

The Low Power
Sprat Book

QRP – the art and science of low-power operation – is one of the most popular aspects of amateur radio.   In the UK, the G QRP Club has been a leading light in this area of operation since its formation in 1974. Its journal, *SPRAT* is recognised as one of the world's leading QRP publications and it has now reached its 150th edition. This milestone is marked by this publication of this book, which is a selection the best of nearly four decades of low-power amateur radio circuits and ideas that have been published in *SPRAT*.

The Low Power Spratbook is divided into seven parts, covering transmitters, receivers, transceivers, antennas, ATUs, Morse keys and keyers, and a section for those circuits which might best be categorised as 'miscellaneous'. Circuits vary in complexity from an "ultra-simple" 80m CW transceiver using just 14 parts to the more sophisticated 'Sparkford', designed by Walford Electronics and also for use on 80m CW. You will find early 'classics' within these pages, including the 'OXO' transmitter and the 'ONER' both GM3OXX designs. *The Low Power Spratbook* also includes QRP classics such as versions of the 'FOXX' transceiver, the 'Pixie', the 'Epiphyte' and the 'Naxos'. All are presented as they were originally printed.

The Low Power Spratbook will appeal to the dedicated QRP enthusiast through to all those who have never tried QRP construction work before. This book is a veritable gold mine of ingenious designs and circuits and provides a superb introduction and reference book dedicated to the art and science of low-power or QRP amateur radio.

Size 174x240mm 320 pages ISBN: 9781 9050 8686 3

RRP £14.99

E&OE All prices shown plus p&p